Nicola Call & Sally F

What Natasha Can Do

Natasha can get her own breakfast and eat it without making a mess.

TJ can't!

Natasha can pour her own milk
and drink from a cup.

TJ can't!

Natasha can go to the toilet on her own and wash her hands.

TJ can't!

Natasha can put on her own coat
and do up the toggles.

TJ can't!

Natasha can put on her boots.

Natasha can get her bag off the shelf.

TJ can't!

Natasha can walk all the
way to school.

TJ can't!

Natasha can splash in puddles...

AND SO CAN TJ!

What Natasha Can Do

Introduction

This story explores some of the many things that Natasha can do independently. She can pour her own milk, fasten her own toggles, use the toilet and wash her hands on her own. Her little brother TJ needs help with all these things. But when it rains, TJ comes into his own and shows that he is just as capable as Natasha – at splashing in puddles!

Top tips for using this book

Remember that you don't need to do them all at once!

1 Read this book aloud to your child, and talk about the pictures. Encourage your child to tell the story in his or her own words. Talk about how Natasha feels about being independent. Talk about how TJ might feel. Does TJ wish that he could do things without help? Does Natasha sometimes wish she had more help from her mum?

2 Encourage your child to do the things that Natasha can do, like pouring her/his own drink, even if it does sometimes make a bit of a mess! Set your child up for success, for example by having small containers for pouring, and keeping cups and bowls on shelves that your child can reach.

3 Make a 'Can-do' list with your child of all the things that she/he can do independently. Play games where you actively teach new skills, and add to the list whenever she/he does something new.

4 Make a collage or book with your child, using pictures cut from baby magazines and catalogues. Talk about how parents help their babies to learn new things. Include some baby photos of your child and siblings or cousins, showing their 'firsts', such as taking their first steps or eating their first foods.

5 When your child is with younger children, encourage him/her to help and to show how independent he/she can be. Give him/her jobs that allow for success, even if it takes a little longer than doing it yourself. On other occasions, allow your child to be the 'baby' – remember that everyone needs a little TLC at times!

6 Turn a corner of a room into a pretend baby clinic, with dolls or soft toys, blankets, wipes and plastic utensils. Play with your child and gradually include new items as you both take care of the 'babies'. Let your child take the lead and think of new ways to develop the game.

Published 2013 by Featherstone Education
An imprint of Bloomsbury Publishing Plc
50 Bedford Square, London, WC1B 3DP
www.bloomsbury.com

ISBN 9781408163894

Text © Nicola Call and Sally Featherstone
Illustrations © Jane Massey

A CIP record for this publication is available from
the British Library.

Printed in China by C & C Offset Printing Co., Ltd.

This book is produced using paper that is made
from wood grown in managed, sustainable
forests. It is natural, renewable and recyclable. The
logging and manufacturing process conform to the
environmental regulations of the country of origin.

10 9 8 7 6 5 4 3 2